Steve Elsworth

SUPPLEMENTARY GRAMMAR EXERCISES 1

OPENING STRATEGIES

Longman

Unit 1

Punctuation

> **Capital letters**
>
> I'm Paul Roberts. Good evening, Mrs Jones. Is your name Peter? My name's Diana.

1 Write the sentences. Use capital letters where necessary.

my name's carlos. what's your name?

My name's Carlos. What's your name?

1 my name's david. what's your name?

....

2 is your name joanne?

....

3 his name's paul.

....

4 good morning, mr hall.

....

5 is her name nina roberts?

....

6 good afternoon, mrs churchill.

....

7 my name's juan. what's your name?

....

Ask questions

2 Write the questions in the boxes.

you/Paul?

Are you Paul?

your name/Jack?

Is your name Jack?

1 you/Sue?

2 your name/John?

3 you/Sally Jones?

4 your name/Tim Trent?

5 your name/Vince?

6 you/Jack Gibbs?

7 you/Mr Porter?

Give answers

3 Write the answers.

What's her name?

(Diana) Her name's Diana.

What's your name?

(Mark) My name's Mark.

1 What's her name?

(Sue) ....

2 What's your name?

(Peter) ....

3 What's his name?

(Gerald Ellis) ....

4 What's your name?

(Sally Jones).....................................

5 What's his name?

(Mr Roberts) ....

6 What's her name?

(Mrs Feldman)...................................

7 What's your name?

(Peter Jackson) ....

4 Write the answers (✓ = Yes, ✗ = No).

Are you Mary Walker?   ✓ Yes, I am.

Are you Robert Taylor?   ✗ No, I'm not.

1 Are you Mark Patterson? ✓ ....

2 Are you Sheila Matty? ✗ ....

3 Are you Ian Teller? ✓ ....

4 Are you Dave Weller? ✓ ....

5 Are you Mrs Feldman? ✓ ....

6 Are you Margaret Penn? ✗ ....

5 Write the answers, using No.

Is your name Roberts?   No, it isn't.

Are you Paul Roberts?   No, I'm not.

1 Is your name Trent? ....

2 Are you Diana Hall? ....

3 Is your name Peter Webb? ....

4 Are you Mark Trent? ....

5 Is your name Matthews? ....

6 Are you Sally Gibbs? ....

7 Are you Mr Taylor? ....

Unit 1

Long and short

Long	Short	
(I am)	I'm	in Room 204.
(You are)	You're	in Room 302.
(Her name is)	Her name's	Diana.
(It is)	It's	Paul Teller.
(I am not)	I'm not	Paul Roberts.
(It is not)	It isn't	Paul Roberts.
(What is)	What's	your name?

6 Write the sentences, using the long form.

I'm in Room 204.

I am in Room 204.
....

1 I'm in Room 307.

....

2 You're in Room 308.

....

3 It's Paul Roberts.

....

4 My name's Sue Teller.

....

5 What's your name?

....

6 No, I'm not.

....

7 No, it isn't.

....

7 Write the short forms in the boxes.

It is Jack Tessler. | It's |

I am John Gibbs. | I'm |

1 *It is* Dianne Gibbs. | |

2 *I am* Jack Feldman. | |

3 *What is* her name? | |

4 Her *name is* Joanne. | |

5 *You are* in Room 9. | |

6 *He is* Mark Boakes. | |

7 *I am* Sue Warren. | |

8 His *name is* Peter. | |

4

Use numbers

8 Write the telephone numbers in the bubbles.

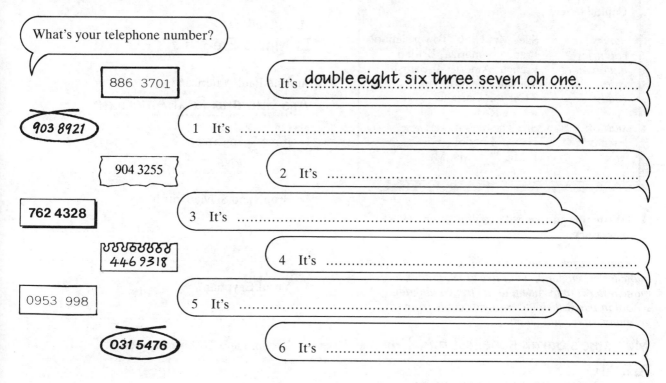

What's your telephone number?

886 3701

It's <u>double eight six three seven oh one.</u>

903 8921

1 It's ....

904 3255

2 It's ....

762 4328

3 It's ....

446 9318

4 It's ....

0953 998

5 It's ....

031 5476

6 It's ....

Grammar summary

9 Write the missing words.

What's	your *his* her	name	My His	name's Pat.

.... you Marie Teller?	Yes, I .... No, ...

Is .... name Peter?	Yes, it .... No, it ....

Unit 2

Punctuation

Capital letters	
names	Sue, Mrs Gibb, Tower School
countries	France, America, Britain
nationalities	French, American, British
cities	Manchester, London
roads	3 Carlton Gardens,
	4 New Road
start of	She's a student.
sentence	He's in London.
other	I, Mr, Mrs, Ms, Miss

1 **Write this passage with capital letters where necessary.**

my name's sarah roberts, and i'm british. i come from manchester, england, and i live at 19, grant road, manchester. i'm a student at the french language school in paris. the other students come from germany, italy, and japan.

My name's Sarah Roberts, and I'm
British.

....

....

....

....

....

....

....

Ask questions

2 **Write questions.**

Marie/French?

Is Marie French ?

....

Sue and Paul/American?

Are Sue and Paul American?

....

1   Jorge/Spanish?

....

2   Bruno and Sylvia/British?

....

....

3   Yusuf/Egyptian?

....

4   Yoshimi and Toshiye/Japanese?

....

....

5   Peter/Mexican?

....

6   Carlos/Brazilian?

....

7   Lois and Frank/French?

....

....

8   Sabine and George/Italian?

....

....

Give answers

3 Write the answers (✓ = *Yes*, ✗ = *No*).

Are you French?	✓	Yes, I am.
Is Miss Grant here?	✗	No, she isn't.
1 Are you Italian?	✓	
2 Are you from Milan?	✗	
3 Is Bruno Spanish?	✓	
4 Is he a student?	✗	
5 Is Miss Jones a teacher?	✓	
6 Is she here?	✗	
7 Is your name Dunn?	✓	
8 Is your name Sue Dunn?	✗	
9 Are Paul and Di French?	✓	
10 Are they from New York?	✗	

Which is which?

4 Write *N* above the nationalities, and *C* above the countries.

　　　　N
I'm American.

　　　　C
They're from France.

1 She's Danish.

2 I'm from Japan.

3 She's English.

4 We're French.

5 I'm from Denmark.

6 He's from Germany.

7 They're from Italy.

8 She's Japanese.

9 They're from Spain.

10 It's a map of Brazil.

Long and short

5 Write the long form of these sentences.

We're here for the conference.
We are here for the conference.
....

....

1 She's a new student.

....

2 He's very polite.

....

3 We're Italian.

....

4 I'm Sylvana.

....

5 It's a small class.

....

6 You're in Room 201.

....

7 They're here for the conference.

....

....

6 Write these sentences in the short form.

She isn't here. .... She is not here.

1 .... They are not French.

2 .... I am not John Porter.

3 .... She is not Italian.

4 .... We are not from Manchester.

5 .... It is not my dictionary.

6 .... He is not British.

7 .... You are not in my class.

Language in use

7 Write *this* or *that* in the bubbles.

Grammar summary

8 Write the missing words.

The present simple: to be

Positive

Long	Short		
I am	(I'm)		
You are	(You're)	from	London. France.
He is	(..................)		
She is	(..................)		
It is	(It's)		
We are	(..................)	British. French.
They are	(They're)		

Questions

Are	.... you	
.... he	from France?
Is	.... she	
.... it	French?
Are	.... they	

Short answers

Positive		Negative	
Yes, I	am.	No, I	'm not.
he	is.	he	isn't.
she	....	she	....
it	....	it	....
we	are.	we	....
they	....	they	aren't.

Unit 3

The present simple

	Positive	Negative	Questions		
I You We They	live here	don't live here. (= do not)	Do	I you we they	live here?
He She It	lives	doesn't live here. (= does not)	Does	he she it	

Ask questions

1 Write the questions.

you/like London?

Do you like London ?

1 you/like Los Angeles?

....

2 Paul/like London?

....

3 they/live in Bristol?

....

4 she/like children?

....

5 you/like your school?

....

6 he/live here?

....

7 Diana/like her job?

....

2 Write the questions using *What* or *Where*.

What do you do ?

I'm a nurse.

Where does he live ?

He lives in Dover.

1 ....

I'm a computer programmer.

2 ....

I live in Liverpool.

3 ....

He's a nurse.

4 ....

He lives in London.

5 ....

She lives in America.

6 ....

She's an artist.

Give answers

3 Write the answers, using *No*.

Do you live in London? (Manchester)

No, I don't live in London.
I live in Manchester.

1 Do you live in Britain? (France)

....

....

2 Does he live in Edinburgh? (Liverpool)

....

....

3 Do you like classical music? (pop music)

....

....

4 Does she like tea? (coffee)

....

....

5 Do they live in the USA? (Mexico)

....

....

6 Does he live in a flat? (a house)

....

....

7 Do they like Chinese food? (Italian food)

....

....

8 Do you live on the south coast? (east coast)

....

....

The present simple: short answers

Positive			Negative		
Yes,	I you we they	do.	No,	I you we they	don't.
	he she it	does.		he she it	doesn't.

4 Write the short answers in the boxes.

Do you work in London? | *Yes, I do.*

Does Mary work in London? | *No, she doesn't.*

1 Do you work in Boston? | *Yes,*

2 Does Mrs Baker work in Boston, too? | *No,*

3 Do the children like Chinese food? | *Yes,*

4 Do they like coffee? | *No,*

5 Does Paul like his job? | *Yes,*

6 Does he like London? | *No,*

7 Does your sister work for a dentist? | *Yes,*

8 Does she like the dentist? | *No,*

9 Do you live in a flat? | *Yes,*

10 Do you work in the flat? | *No,*

11

Unit 3

Word formation

Plurals				
Most words	*Singular* cat dog friend ticket school	+ **s**	*Plural* cats dogs friends tickets schools	
Words ending in -y	baby country secretary	+ **ies**	babies countries secretaries	

5 Write the plurals of the words in the boxes.

friend	friends
secretary	secretaries
purse	
student	
number	
teacher	
dictionary	
baby	
book	
company	
hotel	
country	
pen	
sister	

Punctuation

The apostrophe	
Possession	Mark's name, the girl's mother, Joan's pen
Short form	don't (= do not), doesn't (= does not), I'm (= I am), you're (= you are), it's (= it is), they're (= they are)

6 Write these sentences. Use apostrophes where necessary.

Im Dianas assistant.

I'm Diana's assistant.

1 Im Lucys secretary.

   ....

2 Shes a director.

   ....

3 I dont know.

   ....

4 Paul doesnt like classical music.

   ....

5 You dont like Marys mother, do you?

   ....

6 Theyre French.

   ....

7 She doesnt like coffee.

   ....

Grammar summary

7 Write the words in the correct form.

The present simple

<table>
<tr><td colspan="2">

Positive

I *like* (like) children.

You .... (like) children, too.

He .... (live) here.

She .... (live) in this house.

We .... (work) for a video company.

They .... (work) for a video company, too.

</td><td colspan="2">

Negative

I *don't like* (not like) this flat.

You .... (not like) this flat, do you?

He .... (not work) for this company.

She .... (not work) here.

We .... (not live) there now.

They .... (not like) the school much.

</td></tr>
</table>

<table>
<tr><td>

Questions

(I/do)

What *do I do* ? I'm a doctor.

(you/live)

Where ....?

(he/work)

.... for you?

(she/like)

.... her job?

(we/live)

Where ....? In London.

(they/like)

.... children?

</td><td>

Short answers

	Positive	
Do you like school?	Yes, I	*do.*
Do I live near your flat?	Yes, you	....
Does he like this class?	Yes, he	....
Does she live near here?	Yes, she	....
Do you both work here?	Yes, we	....
Do they like the new job?	Yes, they	....
	Negative	
Do you like Los Angeles?	No, I	*don't.*
Do I live near you?	No, you	....
Does he like this music?	No, he	....
Does she work for Paul?	No, she	....
Do you both live here?	No, we	....
Do they all work here?	No, they	....

</td></tr>
</table>

Unit 4

Ask questions

1 Write the questions in the correct places.

Are you British?	
What's this in English?	
What's your name?	
How old are you?	
How much are the tickets?	
How old is it?	
Are you from New York?	

What's this in English? .... It's a cathedral.

1 .... It's two hundred years old.

2 .... They're £1.50.

3 .... No, I'm not. I'm American.

4 .... No, I'm from Boston.

5 .... My name's Mary Schweitzer.

6 .... I'm eighteen.

Give answers

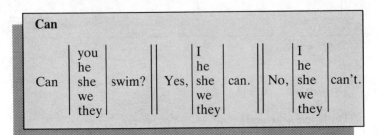

Can

Can	you he she we they	swim?	Yes,	I he she we they	can.	No,	I he she we they	can't.

2 Write the questions or answers in the bubbles.

...... *Can* ...... you ski?

Yes, I can.

Can he swim?

No, he *can't.*

1 .... he drive?

Yes, he can.

2 .... you cook?

No, I can't.

3 .... she swim?

Yes, she can.

4 .... they type?

No, they can't.

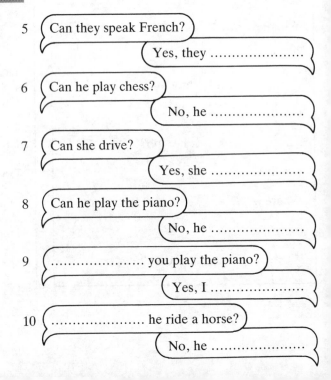

5 Can they speak French?

Yes, they ....

6 Can he play chess?

No, he ....

7 Can she drive?

Yes, she ....

8 Can he play the piano?

No, he ....

9 .... you play the piano?

Yes, I ....

10 .... he ride a horse?

No, he ....

14

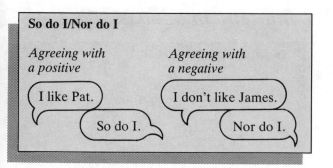

So do I/Nor do I

Agreeing with a positive

I like Pat.

So do I.

Agreeing with a negative

I don't like James.

Nor do I.

3 Agree with the statements.

I like Mary.   So do I.

I don't like Jack.   Nor do I.

1 I like Mrs Green.

2 I don't like her sister.

3 I hate seeing her.

4 She smokes a lot.
   I don't like that.

5 I don't like her
   children.

6 I like Mrs Green's
   children.

Word formation

I/Me/My

Subject	I	you	he	she	it	we	they
Object	me	you	him	her	it	us	them
Adjective	my	your	his	her	its	our	their

Subject		Object			Adjective	
I	like	you.			my	
She	likes	me.	It's	your		book.
We	like	them.			his	

4 Write these words in the correct sentences below.

his her our their him her us them he she we they I

....I.... live here. It's my house.

1 .... live here. It's our house.

2 Her name's Sheila. .... works here.

3 His name's Peter Hanson. ....'s a doctor.

4 ....'re students, and they all come from Argentina.

5 Do you like John Patterson? I like ....

6 How about Brigitte? Do you like ....?

7 And my parents? Do you like ....?

8 How about me and my sister?

   Do you like ....?

9 This is my sister. .... name's Kathy.

10 And my brother. .... name's Justin.

11 They're Americans. Do you like .... clothes?

12 We like Mr and Mrs Fallon. They're .... friends.

15

Unit 4

This/That/These/Those

		here	there	
Singular	How much is	this	that	book?
Plural	How much are	these	those	books?

5 Circle the correct answer.

How much is (this)/those/these record?

1 How much is *this/those/these* dictionary?

2 How much are *these/those/this* cakes over there?

3 How much is *this/those/these* tea?

4 How much are *these/this/that* chocolates?

5 How much is *this/these/those* ticket?

6 I like *this/that/these* cups. How much are they?

7 *This/These/Those* cheese is nice. How much is it?

8 How much are *this/these/those* diaries there?

9 I like *that/those/these* record.

10 Do you want *this/that/these* biscuits?

Use numbers

6 Write the numbers.

22	twenty-two
34	
45	
56	
21	

12	
99	
87	
78	
67	
19	

Language in use

Love/Like/Don't like/Hate

		Nouns
I	like don't like hate love	school. London.
		Verbs + -ing swimming. working here.

7 Write the sentences in the correct order.

doesn't/Coke/she/like

She doesn't like Coke.

letters/hates/writing/he

He hates writing letters.

1 cheese/I/like/sandwiches/don't

2 the/loves/to/she/theatre/going

3 discos/father/hates/my

4 television/like/watching/don't/I

5 my/sightseeing/like/doesn't/sister

6 cake/love/chocolate/I

16

Grammar summary

8 Write the missing words.

How old ....is........ he?	He's .... 22.
How old ....she?	She .... 24.
How old .... it?	It .... a hundred years old.
How old .... you?	I .... 20.

I	like	(go)	going............ to school.
	don't like	(watch)	.... television.
	love	(go)	.... to discos.
	hate	(sit)	.... in cafes.
He She	hates	(write)	writing........ letters.
	likes	(play)	.... chess.
	loves	(play)	.... the piano.

Can	you	drive?	Yes, I can.................	No, I can't.............
	he	type?	Yes, he	No, he ....
	she	swim?	Yes, she	No, she ....

Unit 5 Consolidation

1 Write the sentences, using capital letters, apostrophes and full stops where necessary.

my names carole im a teacher in the tower school in london its a good school and i like working there i live in a flat in the centre of town the flats small but very nice i like it very much

My name's Carole. ....

....

....

....

2 Write the short answers in the bubbles.

Do you like sightseeing?
Yes, I do.

Can you speak English?
No, I can't.

1 Do you like driving?
Yes, ...

2 Can you swim?
No, ...

3 Are you Italian?
Yes, ...

4 Do you live here?
No, ...

5 Can you speak English?
Yes, ...

6 Do you like sightseeing?
No, ...

7 Is your name Roberto?
Yes, ...

8 Are you Roberto Fabriani?
No, ...

9 Are you a student?
Yes, ...

10 Do you like London?
No, ...

3 Write the questions.

How old is it ? ....
It's twenty years old.

1 ....
It's a hundred years old.

2 ....
It's £1.50.

3 ....
My name's Diana Roberts.

4 ....
I'm a student.

5 ....
I'm 23.

6 ....
Yes, I live in London.

7 ....
Yes, I like living here.

8 ....
No, I can't drive.

9 ....
No, I don't work here.

10 ....
Yes, I like chocolate.

18

4 Write the answers, using *No*.

Is she a secretary? (doctor)

No, she isn't a secretary.

She's a doctor.

1 Does she work in London? (in Paris)

....

....

2 Is she the director? (her assistant)

....

....

3 Can she speak German? (French and Italian)

....

....

4 Does she live here? (with her brother)

....

....

5 Is her sister's name Margaret? (Julia)

....

....

6 Does Julia work here? (in America)

....

....

7 Does Julia live in New York? (San Francisco)

....

....

8 Can Julia speak German? (Spanish)

....

....

5 Write the numbers.

fourteen	14	twelve	
a thousand		twenty	
eighty		a hundred	
seventy-three		forty	
eighteen		fifteen	
forty-nine		thirty-seven	
a million		ninety-four	
fifty		eleven	

6 Circle the correct answer.

He *a) don't* *b) doesn't* *c) isn't* live here.

1 She *a) 's* *b) 'm* *c) does* a teacher.

2 How much are *a) these* *b) this* *c) that* biscuits?

3 I *a) 'm not* *b) can't* *c) isn't* play the piano.

4 *a) Are* *b) Is* *c) Do* you like football?

5 He lives *a) at* *b) to* *c) in* London.

6 They *a) doesn't* *b) don't* *c) aren't* live here.

7 She doesn't like *a) my* *b) I* *c) me*.

8 She's *a) our* *b) us* *c) we* teacher.

9 Where *a) does* *b) do* *c) are* they live?

10 He's *a) France* *b) Germany* *c) Italian*.

11 How much *a) do* *b) is* *c) are* that map?

12 Can I have a *a) cup* *b) glass* *c) piece* of cake?

13 Mark *a) likes* *b) don't like* *c) like* me.

14 *a) Are* *b) Can* *c) Do* they from Spain?

15 I *a) can't* *b) 'm not* *c) don't* Spanish.

19

Unit 6

1 Complete the questions using *Was* or *Were*.

<u>Were</u>........ you at the meeting yesterday?

1 .... they at the conference last week?

2 .... Diana there too?

3 .... Mr and Mrs May here last night?

4 .... Mark at your house yesterday?

5 .... you at the meeting this morning?

6 .... the meeting interesting?

7 .... the cassettes interesting?

8 .... the film very funny?

Give answers

2 Write the short answers in the bubbles.

Were you at home last night?

Yes, I was.

Were your parents at home?

No, they weren't.

1 Were you here yesterday?

Yes, ...

2 Were your friends with you?

No, ...

3 Was Diana at home last night?

No, ...

4 Was Peter at school last week?

Yes, ...

5 Were your parents at a restaurant last night?

Yes, ...

6 Was the meeting interesting?

No, ...

7 Were the children at home last night?

No, ...

8 Were you at the party yesterday?

No, ...

Use your dictionary

Countables and uncountables

You can count some things. These are called *countable nouns*.

Other things are difficult to count. These are called *uncountable nouns*.

Most nouns are countable.
In a dictionary [U] = uncountable.

or·ange¹ /'ɒrɪndʒ‖'ɔː-, 'ɑ-/ n
a very common reddish-yellow round fruit

sug·ar¹ /'ʃʊgəʳ/ n [U] a
sweet substance obtained
from plants

A, an, some

Countable nouns	*Uncountable nouns*
a pencil	some toothpaste
an orange	some water

4 Write *a, an* or *some* in the spaces.

I want to buy ....*a*.............. ticket.

I want to buy ....*some*.......... toothpaste.

I want to buy ....*an*............. orange.

1   Can I have .... ticket, please?

2   Can I have .... toothpaste, please?

3   He wants to buy .... newspaper.

4   I want to go to .... bank.

5   He wants to get .... milk.

6   She wants to get .... money.

7   I want to buy .... postcard.

8   I want to get .... water.

9   Can I have .... umbrella, please?

10 Can I have .... sugar, please?

3 *Water* is an uncountable noun. Write *U* next to the other seven uncountable nouns. Check in your dictionary if you're not sure.

cup		cassette	
water	U	flower	
sandwich		toothpaste	
stamp		wine	
soap		box	
money		sugar	
cheese		bus	
milk		postcard	

Language in use

5 Use the information to complete the conversation.

What time *does the bus leave school ?*
It leaves school at nine o'clock.

1 What time ....?
It arrives in London at quarter past eleven.

2 What time ....?
The concert starts at half past twelve.

3 And when ....?
It finishes at quarter to two.

4 What time ....?
The cinema opens at three o'clock.

5 And when ....?
The film starts at half past three.

6 Oh. When ....?
It finishes at quarter to six.

7 When does the bus leave London?

It ....

8 When does it arrive at school?

It ....

```
SCHOOL TRIP

Bus leaves school at 09.00

    arrives in London at 11.15

Concert starts at 12.30

        finishes at 13.45

Cinema opens at 15.00

Film starts at 15.30

    finishes at 17.45

Bus leaves London at 19.15

    arrives at school at 21.30


Note:  Bank opens at 10.00

        closes at 15.30!
```

9 Thank you. Oh, what time does the bank open?

It ....

10 And when does it close?

It ....

6 Read the directions, starting from the point marked ✕. Write the number of each place on the map.

1 Turn left at the flower shop, and
  it's on your right.
2 Turn left at the flower shop, and
  it's on your left.
3 Turn right at the flower shop,
  and it's on your left.
4 Turn right at the cinema, and
  it's on your right.
5 Turn left at the cinema, and it's
  on your left.
6 Turn right at the cinema, and
  it's on your left.
7 Turn right at the flower shop,
  and it's on your right.
8 Turn left at the cinema, and it's
  on your right.

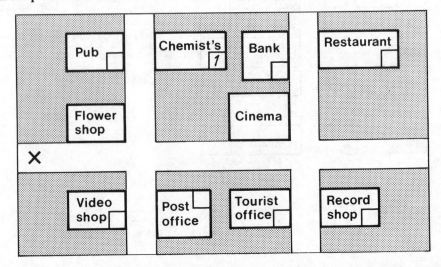

Use numbers

7 Write the times, using *to* and *past*.

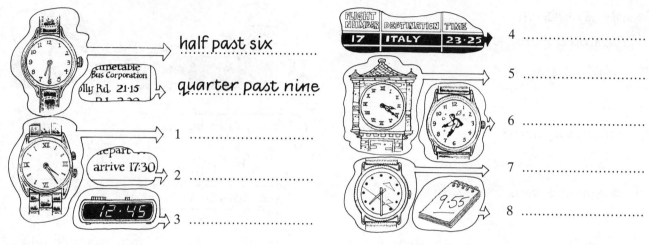

half past six

quarter past nine

1 ....

2 ....

3 ....

4 ....

5 ....

6 ....

7 ....

8 ....

Grammar summary

8 Write the missing words.

The past simple: to be

Positive

I	was	
You	were	
He	....	
She	....	at the office yesterday.
We	....	
They	....	

Questions

Was	I	
Were	you	
....	he	at the meeting
....	she	last week?
....	we	
....	they	

Short answers

	Positive		Negative	
Yes, I	was	No, I	wasn't
you	were	you	....
he	....	he	....
she	....	she	....
we	....	we	....
they	....	they	....

Unit 7

Ask questions

1 Write the questions, using *Have* or *Has*.

you/got/any children?

Have you got any children?

1 you/got/any sisters?

   ....

2 Susan/got/any sisters?

   ....

3 she/got/any brothers?

   ....

4 Peter and Diane/got/any American friends?

   ....

5 they/got/any British friends?

   ....

6 you/got/any British friends?

   ....

7 Mr Abbott/got/any brothers?

   ....

8 he/got/any sisters?

   ....

Give answers

2 Write the answers in the bubbles.

What are you doing?

(watch television)

I'm watching television.

1 And what's Marie doing?

   (read the paper)

   ....

2 Oh. And Peter? What's he doing?

   (listen to records)

   ....

3 How about your mother?

   (read a book)

   ....

4 And your father?

   (sleep)

   ....

5 What's Patrick doing?

   (visit friends)

   ....

6 Oh. What are his parents doing, then?

   (sightsee)

   ....

7 That's nice. Is his sister with them?

   (Listen to records with Peter)

   ....
   ....

Long and short

Present continuous	Have got	
I'm (=I am) working.	I've (=I have) got	
You're (=You are) reading.	You've (=You have) got	
He's (=He is) talking.	He's (=He has) got	
She's (=She is) sleeping.	She's (=She has) got	a son.
We're (=We are) going.	We've (=We have) got	
They're (=They are) leaving.	They've (=They have) got	

3 Write the long form.

(I'm sitting) ..I am sitting.......................... here.

1 (She's jogging) ....

2 (We're doing) .... exercises.

3 (They're playing) .... tennis.

4 (You're reading) .... my newspaper.

5 (I'm working) ....

4 Write the long form.

(I've got) ..I have got........................... a son and a daughter.

1 (Mary's got) .... three children.

2 (We've got) .... two daughters.

3 (They've got) .... four sons and a daughter.

4 (He's got) .... a daughter called Sue.

5 (I've got) .... five sisters.

6 (I haven't got) .... any children.

7 (He hasn't got) .... any brothers.

Unit 7

Which is which?

5 Write *is* or *has* in the boxes.

She's got two sisters.

He's sleeping.

1 Marie's got three brothers.

2 Paul's watching television.

3 Mr Hall's talking to Anne.

4 She's got a sister and two brothers.

5 He's reading a newspaper.

6 Mark's got three children.

7 Diana's got a daughter called Delia.

has
is

Word formation

> **Verbs + *ing***
> Most verbs just add *ing*:
> watch + **ing** = watching
> play + **ing** = playing
> Verbs ending in one *e* lose the *e*:
> drive + **ing** = driving
> ride + **ing** = riding

6 Write the *ing* form of the verb.

watch *watching*   4 talk ....

arrive *arriving*   5 ride ....

1 play ....   6 listen ....

2 type ....   7 visit ....

3 leave ....   8 smoke ....

Language in use

7 Describe Cathy's routine. Use the notes.

> M   visit Jane
> T   go to college
> W   go swimming
> Th   go shopping
> F   play squash
> Sa   play football
> Su   look after Jane's baby

On Monday, she visits Jane.

1 ....

2 ....

3 ....

4 ....

5 ....

6 ....

8 Describe the weather. Make words from the jumbled letters.

What's the weather like?

It's *very cold* .... (evry locd)

1 .... (revy tho)

2 .... (etiqu icne)

3 .... (gninira)

4 .... (uqite rawm)

5 .... (wosnnig)

6 .... (loudcy)

7 .... (ynnus)

Grammar summary

9 Write the missing words.

The present continuous

Positive

I   'm reading. (read)

You   .... (work)

He   .... (go)

She   .... (study)

We   .... (leave)

They   .... (talk)

Questions

What

..... am I   doing? (do)

..... are ..... you   reading? (read)

.... he   .... (cook)

.... she   .... (paint)

.... we   .... (do)

.... they..................... (make)

Have got

Positive

I   've got

He   ....

She   ....   two children.

We   ....

They   ....

Negative

I   haven't got

He   ....

She   ....   any children.

We   ....

They   ....

Questions

..... Have ..... you   ..... got .....

.... he   ....

.... she   ....   a sister?

.... they   ....

Unit 8

Give answers

1 Write the answers.

Do you ever go to work by underground? (Yes/often) ...... Yes, I often go to work by underground.

1   Do you ever go to work by bus? (Yes/sometimes) ....

2   Do you ever walk to work? (No/never) ....

3   Do you ever work on Saturday? (Yes/usually) ....

4   Are you ever late for work? (No/never) ....

5   Do you ever work on Sunday? (Yes/sometimes) ....

6   Do you ever study in the evening? (Yes/often) ....

2 Give answers about Carolyn's routine.

February

Monday	Tuesday	Wednesday	Thursday	Friday	Saturday	Sunday
1 exercises	2 tennis	3 exercises	4 cinema	5 volleyball	6 volleyball	7 church parents
8 exercises	9 tennis	10 exercises	11 disco	12 volleyball	13 volleyball	14 church parents
15 exercises	16 tennis	17 exercises	18 cinema	19 volleyball	20 volleyball	21 church parents
22 exercises	23 tennis	24 exercises	25 London	26 volleyball	27 volleyball	28 church parents

How often does she play tennis?

She plays tennis once a week. ...

How often does she go to the cinema?

She goes to the cinema twice a month. ...

1   How often does she play volleyball?

....

2   How often does she go to London?

....

3   How often does she visit her parents?

....

4   How often does she go to a disco?

....

5   How often does she go to church?

....

6   How often does she do exercises?

....

Ask questions

3 Write the questions in the correct places.

> Would you like some wine?
> How far is it?
> How long does it take?
> Is this your room?
> How often do you go by bus?
> Are you ever late for work?
> What sort of wine would you like?
> Does Mary sit here?
> How do you get to work?

Would you like some wine?
....
Yes, please.

1 ....
Red, please.

2 ....
No, my room's on the second floor.

3 ....
No, she sits over there.

4 ....
Usually by bus.

5 ....
Yes, sometimes.

6 ....
About five kilometres.

7 ....
About twenty-five minutes.

8 ....
Three or four times a week.

Singular and plural

There is/There are

	Singular	Plural	
Positive	There's a bedroom. (=There is)	There are	two / some bedrooms.
Negative	There isn't a toilet. (=There is not)	There aren't any toilets. (=There are not)	

4 Write *there's, there are, there isn't* or *there aren't* in the bubbles.

> Is there a garden?
> Yes, **there's** a big garden.

> Is there a basement?
> No, **there isn't** a basement.

1 > Is there a nice kitchen?
> Yes, ... a lovely kitchen.

2 > Is there a study?
> No, ... a study.

3 > And big bedrooms?
> Yes, ... three big bedrooms.

4 > How about stairs?
> No, ... any stairs.

5 > How many toilets?
> .... two toilets.

6 > How about bathrooms?
> .... a small bathroom.

Unit 8

Countable and uncountable

5 Write *C* by the countable nouns, and *U* by the uncountable nouns.
Check in your dictionary if you're not sure.

tomato	C
milk	U

1	potato	
2	beer	
3	vegetable	

4	pork	
5	beef	
6	carrot	

7	meat	
8	sandwich	
9	apple	

10	lager	
11	bean	
12	biscuit	

A, some

	Countable	Uncountable
Singular	a biscuit	some milk
Plural	some biscuits	

There's	a biscuit some milk	here.	Would you like	a biscuit? some milk?
There are	some biscuits			some biscuits?

6 Write *a* or *some* in the spaces.

There's ....*a*.......... tomato on the table.

Would you like ....*some*........ tomatoes?

There's ....*some*........ sugar here.

1 There are .... potatoes here.

2 There's .... beef in the fridge.

3 There's .... beer in the kitchen.

4 There are .... apples in the garden.

5 Would you like .... biscuit?

6 Would you like .... lager?

7 Would you like .... peas?

8 Would you like .... vegetables?

9 Would you like .... meat?

10 Would you like .... sandwich?

Language in use

7 What colour are they? Write the colours.

.... red ....

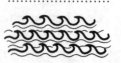

1 ....

4 ....

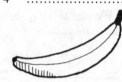

2 ....

5 ....

3 ....

6 ....

Answers

There are 75 points in each unit. Score 1 point for each correct answer (more if the instructions say so).

Unit 1

1 1 My name's David. What's your name? 2 Is your name Joanne? 3 His name's Paul. 4 Good morning, Mr Hall. 5 Is her name Nina Roberts? 6 Good afternoon, Mrs Churchill. 7 My name's Juan. What's your name? *[7]*

2 1 Are you Sue? 2 Is your name John? 3 Are you Sally Jones? 4 Is your name Tim Trent? 5 Is your name Vince? 6 Are you Jack Gibbs? 7 Are you Mr Porter? *[7]*

3 1 Her name's Sue. 2 My name's Peter. 3 His name's Gerald Ellis. 4 My name's Sally Jones. 5 His name's Mr Roberts. 6 Her name's Mrs Feldman. 7 My name's Peter Jackson. *[7]*

4 1 Yes, I am. 2 No, I'm not. 3 Yes, I am. 4 No, I'm not. 5 Yes, I am. 6 No, I'm not. *[6]*

5 1 No, it isn't. 2 No, I'm not. 3 No, it isn't. 4 No, I'm not. 5 No, it isn't. 6 No, I'm not. 7 No, I'm not. *[7]*

6 1 I am in Room 307. 2 You are in Room 308. 3 It is Paul Roberts. 4 My name is Sue Teller. 5 What is your name? 6 No, I am not. 7 No, it is not. *[7]*

7 1 It's 2 I'm 3 What's 4 name's 5 You're 6 He's 7 I'm 8 name's *[8]*

8. (three points each answer) 1 nine oh three eight nine two one 2 nine oh four three two double five (*or* five five) 3 seven six two four three two eight 4 double four (*or* four four) six nine three one eight 5 oh nine five three double nine (*or* nine nine) eight 6 oh three one five four seven six *[18]*

9 *Her* name's Pat. *Are* you Marie Teller? Yes, I *am*. No, *I'm not*. Is *your* name Peter? Yes, it *is*. No, it *isn't*. *[8]*

Unit 2

1 **(One point for each capital letter.)**
I come from Manchester, England, and I live at 19, Grant Road, Manchester. I'm a student at the French Language School in Paris. The other students come from Germany, Italy, and Japan. *[16]*

2 1 Is Jorge Spanish? 2 Are Bruno and Sylvia British? 3 Is Yusuf Egyptian? 4 Are Yoshimi and Toshiye Japanese? 5 Is Peter Mexican? 6 Is Carlos Brazilian? 7 Are Lois and Frank French? 8 Are Sabine and George Italian? *[8]*

3 1 Yes, I am. 2 No, I'm not. 3 Yes, he is. 4 No, he isn't. 5 Yes, she is. 6 No, she isn't. 7 Yes, it is. 8 No, it isn't. 9 Yes, they are. 10 No, they aren't. *[10]*

4 1 Danish (N) 2 Japan (C) 3 English (N) 4 French (N) 5 Denmark (C) 6 Germany (C) 7 Italy (C) 8 Japanese (N) 9 Spain (C) 10 Brazil (C) *[10]*

5 1 She is a new student. 2 He is very polite. 3 We are Italian. 4 I am Sylvana. 5 It is a small class. 6 You are in Room 201. 7 They are here for the conference. *[7]*

6 1 They aren't French. 2 I'm not John Porter. 3 She isn't Italian. 4 We aren't from Manchester. 5 It isn't my dictionary. 6 He isn't British. 7 You aren't in my class. *[7]*

7 1 this 2 that 3 that 4 this 5 this 6 that *[6]*

8 He's She's We're
Is he Is it
she is it is they are she isn't it isn't we aren't *[11]*

Unit 3

1 1 Do you like Los Angeles? 2 Does Paul like London? 3 Do they live in Bristol? 4 Does she like children? 5 Do you like your school? 6 Does he live here? 7 Does Diana like her job? *[7]*

2 1 What do you do? 2 Where do you live? 3 What does he do? 4 Where does he live? 5 Where does she live? 6 What does she do? *[6]*

3 1 No, I don't live in Britain. I live in France. 2 No, he doesn't live in Edinburgh. He lives in Liverpool. 3 No, I don't like classical music. I like pop music. 4 No, she doesn't like tea. She likes coffee. 5 No, they don't live in the USA. They live in Mexico. 6 No, he doesn't live in a flat. He lives in a house. 7 No, they don't like Chinese food. They like Italian food. 8 No, I don't live on the south coast. I live on the east coast. *[8]*

4 1 Yes, I do. 2 No, she doesn't. 3 Yes, they do. 4 No, they don't. 5 Yes, he does. 6 No, he doesn't. 7 Yes, she does. 8 No, she doesn't. 9 Yes, I do. 10 No, I don't. *[10]*

5 purses students numbers teachers dictionaries babies books companies hotels countries pens sisters *[12]*

6 1 I'm Lucy's secretary. 2 She's a director. 3 I don't know. 4 Paul doesn't like classical music. 5 You don't like Mary's mother, do you? 6 They're French. 7 She doesn't like coffee. *[7]*

7 You like He lives She lives We work They work
You don't like He doesn't work She doesn't work We don't live They don't like
do you live Does he work Does she like do we live Do they like
Yes, you do. Yes, he does. Yes, she does. Yes, we do. Yes, they do.
No, you don't. No, he doesn't. No, she doesn't. No, we don't. No, they don't. *[25]*

Unit 4

1 1 How old is it? 2 How much are the tickets? 3 Are you British? 4 Are you from New York? 5 What's your name? 6 How old are you? *[6]*

2 1 Can he drive? 2 Can you cook? 3 Can she swim? 4 Can they type? 5 Yes, they can. 6 No, he can't. 7 Yes, she can. 8 No, he can't. 9 Can you play the piano? Yes, I can. 10 Can he ride a horse? No, he can't. *[10]*

3 1 So do I. 2 Nor do I. 3 So do I. 4 Nor do I. 5 Nor do I. 6 So do I. *[6]*

4 1 We 2 She 3 He 4 They 5 him 6 her 7 them 8 us 9 Her 10 His 11 their 12 our *[12]*

5 1 this 2 those 3 this 4 these 5 this 6 these 7 This 8 those 9 that 10 these *[10]*

6 thirty-four forty-five fifty-six twenty-one twelve ninety-nine eighty-seven seventy-eight sixty-seven nineteen *[10]*

7 1 I don't like cheese sandwiches. 2 She loves going to the theatre. 3 My father hates discos. 4 I don't like watching television. 5 My sister doesn't like sightseeing. 6 I love chocolate cake. *[6]*

8 is she is it are you
She's It's I'm
watching going sitting playing playing
he can she can he can't she can't *[15]*

Unit 5

1 (One point for each capital letter, full stop, or apostrophe.)
I'm a teacher in the Tower School in London. It's a good school and I like working there. I live in a flat in the centre of town. The flat's small but very nice. I like it very much. *[17]*

2 1 Yes, I do. 2 No, I can't. 3 Yes, I am. 4 No, I don't. 5 Yes, I can. 6 No, I don't. 7 Yes, it is. 8 No, I'm not. 9 Yes, I am. 10 No, I don't. *[10]*

3 1 How old is it? 2 How much is it? 3 What's your name? 4 What do you do? 5 How old are you? 6 Do you live in London? (*or* Do you live in Britain?) 7 Do you like London? (*or* Do you like it?) 8 Can you drive? 9 Do you work here? 10 Do you like chocolate? *[10]*

4 1 No, she doesn't work in London. She works in Paris. 2 No, she isn't the director. She's her assistant. 3 No, she can't speak German. She can speak French and Italian. 4 No, she doesn't live here. She lives with her brother. 5 No, her sister's name isn't Margaret. It's Julia. 6 No, Julia doesn't work here. She works in America. 7 No, Julia doesn't live in New York. She lives in San Francisco. 8 No, Julia can't speak German. She can speak Spanish. *[8]*

5 fourteen 14 a thousand 1,000 eighty 80 seventy-three 73 eighteen 18 forty-nine 49 a million 1,000,000 fifty 50 twelve 12 twenty 20 a hundred 100 forty 40 fifteen 15 thirty-seven 37 ninety-four 94 eleven 11 *[15]*

6 1 a) 2 a) 3 b) 4 c) 5 c) 6 b) 7 c) 8 a) 9 b) 10 c) 11 b) 12 c) 13 a) 14 a) 15 b) *[15]*

Unit 6

1 1 Were 2 Was 3 Were 4 Was 5 Were 6 Was 7 Were 8 Was *[8]*

2 1 Yes, I was. 2 No, they weren't. 3 No, she wasn't. 4 Yes, he was. 5 Yes, they were. 6 No, it wasn't. 7 No, they weren't. 8 No, I wasn't. *[8]*

3 soap U money U cheese U milk U toothpaste U wine U sugar U *[7]*

4 1 a 2 some 3 a 4 a 5 some 6 some 7 a 8 some 9 an 10 some *[10]*

5 1 What time does it arrive in London? 2 What time does the concert start? 3 And when does it finish? 4 What time does the cinema open? 5 And when does the film start? 6 Oh. When does it finish? 7 It leaves London at quarter past seven. 8 It arrives at school at half past nine. 9 It opens at ten o'clock. 10 It closes at half past three. *[10]*

6 2 pub 3 post office 4 tourist office 5 bank 6 record shop 7 video shop 8 restaurant *[7]*

7 1 twenty-five past four (*or* four twenty-five) 2 half past five (*or* five thirty) 3 quarter to one (*or* twelve forty-five) 4 twenty-five past eleven (*or* eleven twenty-five) 5 twenty past three (*or* three twenty) 6 twenty-five to nine (*or* eight thirty-five) 7 half past seven (*or* seven thirty) 8 five to ten (*or* nine fifty-five) *[8]*

8 He was She was We were They were
Was he Was she Were we Were they
Yes, he was. Yes, she was. Yes, we were. Yes, they were.
No, you weren't. No, he wasn't. No, she wasn't. No, we weren't. No, they weren't. *[17]*

Unit 7

1 1 Have you got any sisters? 2 Has Susan got any sisters? 3 Has she got any brothers? 4 Have Peter and Diane got any American friends? 5 Have they got any British friends? 6 Have you got any British friends? 7 Has Mr Abbott got any brothers? 8 Has he got any sisters? *[8]*

2 1 She's reading the paper. 2 He's listening to records. 3 She's reading a book. 4 He's sleeping. 5 He's visiting friends. 6 They're sightseeing. 7 She's listening to records with Peter. *[7]*

3 1 She is jogging. 2 We are doing exercises. 3 They are playing tennis. 4 You are reading my newspaper. 5 I am working. *[5]*

4 1 Mary has got 2 We have got 3 They have got 4 He has got 5 I have got 6 I have not got 7 He has not got *[7]*

5 1 has 2 is 3 is 4 has 5 is 6 has 7 has *[7]*

6 1 playing 2 typing 3 leaving 4 talking 5 riding 6 listening 7 visiting 8 smoking *[8]*

7 1 On Tuesday she goes to college. 2 On Wednesday she goes swimming. 3 On Thursday she goes shopping. 4 On Friday she plays squash. 5 On Saturday she plays football. 6 On Sunday she looks after Jane's baby. *[6]*

8 1 It's very hot. 2 It's quite nice. 3 It's raining. 4 It's quite warm. 5 It's snowing. 6 It's cloudy. 7 It's sunny. *[7]*

9 You're working. He's going. She's studying. We're leaving. They're talking.
What's (*or* What is) he cooking? What's (*or* What is) she painting?
What are we doing? What are they making?
He's got She's got We've got They've got
He hasn't got She hasn't got We haven't got They haven't got
Has he got Has she got Have they got *[20]*

Unit 8

1 1 Yes, I sometimes go to work by bus. 2 No, I never walk to work. 3 Yes, I usually work on Saturday. 4 No, I'm never late for work. 5 Yes, I sometimes work on Sunday. 6 Yes, I often study in the evening. *[6]*

2 1 She plays volleyball twice a week. 2 She goes to London once a month. 3 She visits her parents once a week. 4 She goes to a disco once a month. 5 She goes to church once a week. 6 She does exercises twice a week. *[6]*

3 1 What sort of wine would you like? 2 Is this your room? 3 Does Mary sit here? 4 How do you get to work? 5 Are you ever late for work? 6 How far is it? 7 How long does it take? 8 How often do you go by bus? *[8]*

4 1 there's 2 there isn't 3 there are 4 there aren't 5 There are 6 There's *[6]*

5 1 potato C 2 beer U 3 vegetable C 4 pork U 5 beef U 6 carrot C 7 meat U 8 sandwich C 9 apple C 10 lager U 11 bean C 12 biscuit C *[12]*

6 1 some 2 some 3 some 4 some 5 a 6 some 7 some 8 some 9 some 10 a *[10]*

7 1 blue 2 white 3 green 4 black 5 yellow 6 orange *[6]*

8 (One point for each correct answer.) My name's Kevin Tandey and I live in Manchester. I'm a student at Manchester College of Art. I'm staying at (*or* in) a hostel some mile from the centre of town. I usualy go to college by bus, but sometimes I go by car. It takes about half an hour.
At the weekend I usually stay in my room and work. I like talking to the other students, and we sometimes go to a disco or a pub, but I usually stay at home and study. I like my work, it's interesting *[10]*

9 It's about a mile.
How long does the journey take? It takes about ten minutes.
How do you get to work?
How does he/she get to work?

I always/usually/often/sometimes go by car.
He/She always/usually/often/sometimes/goes by bus.
Every day.
Once/Twice a week.

Would you like a sandwich or some salad?
Yes, please. I'd like a sandwich.   [11]

Unit 9

1 1 Did you like the parks? 2 Did you like the Tower of London? 3 Did your parents enjoy the sightseeing? 4 Did they like the Tower? 5 Did your sister like the cafes? 6 Did Peter enjoy the meal?   [6]

2 1 No, I didn't. 2 Yes, he did. 3 No, they didn't. 4 Yes, they did. 5 Yes, she did. 6 No, he didn't. 7 No, I didn't. 8 Yes, she did.   [8]

3 1 Yes, I liked Pat and Mark, but I didn't like the others. 2 Well, I liked the reggae, but I didn't like the other music. 3 I liked the garden, but I didn't like the house. 4 I liked her daughter, but I didn't like her sons. 5 I liked the restaurant, but I didn't like the food.   [5]

4 1 come **V** 2 take **V** 3 cup **N** 4 sit **V** 5 beef **N** 6 listen **V** 7 lunch **N** 8 fruit **N** 9 see **V** 10 pen **N** 11 beer **N** 12 ask **V**   [12]

5 1 to 2 some 3 to 4 to 5 to 6 a 7 a 8 some 9 some 10 to   [10]

6 1 30th 2 17th 3 2nd 4 1st 5 4th 6 20th 7 15th 8 31st   [8]

7 1 on 2 in 3 on 4 in 5 in 6 on 7 in   [7]

8 He enjoyed She liked We enjoyed They liked
Paul didn't enjoy Sue didn't like We didn't like
They didn't like
Did he enjoy Did she like Did we enjoy Did they like
she did we did they did
he didn't she didn't we didn't they didn't   [19]

Unit 10

1 (One point for each capital letter, full stop, or apostrophe.)
He's unemployed. He lives in a friend's house in London. He doesn't like London because it's too big. He wants to go back to Liverpool but he can't because there are no jobs there. Liverpool is still his favourite town.   [18]

2 1 Do 2 Are 3 Is 4 does 5 are 6 do 7 does 8 are 9 Is 10 does   [10]

3 1 did 2 was 3 were 4 did 5 were 6 was 7 were 8 did   [8]

4 1 three forty-five (or quarter to four) 2 fourth 3 one pound fifty 4 forty-eight 5 eleven-thirty five (or twenty-five to twelve) 6 second 7 thirty-first 8 half 9 two twenty (or twenty past two) 10 quarter   [10]

5 you your him his her her it its (not it's) us our them their   [12]

6 1 a) 2 c) 3 b) 4 c) 5 b) 6 c) 7 a) 8 c) 9 c) 10 b)   [10]

7 B How far is it to Edinburgh? About thirty miles. C Why didn't you like the film? It was too long. D How often does she go abroad? About once a month. E Is there a bank near here? Yes, there's one over there. F What's the weather like? It's raining. G Isn't it a lovely day? Yes, it's very nice. H What shall we do today? Let's go to the beach.   [7]

Unit 11

1 1 When are you going? 2 Which airport are you leaving from? 3 How long are you staying in Athens? 4 Where are you staying? 5 When are you coming back? 6 What time are you arriving? 7 How are you getting home? 8 When are you seeing Mrs Harris?   [8]

2 (One point for each correct picture.)
2 That's lovely. How much does it cost? 3 Can I try one on? 4 I'm afraid it's too big. Have you got a Small size? 5 This is too small. Have you got a Medium size? 6 I'll have this one. Can I pay by cheque?   [5]

3 1 Yes, it is. 2 Yes, they are, 3 Yes, he is. 4 Yes, she is. 5 Yes, I am. 6 Yes, we are. 7 Yes, he is. 8 Yes, they are.   [8]

4 tours journeys coaches cities keys families holidays videos beaches cinemas glasses dances boys windows cheques   [15]

5 women programmes housewives potatoes relatives days men cassettes dresses discos   [10]

6 3 **B** 4 **G** 5 **J** 6 **I** 7 **A** 8 **C** 9 **F** 10 **K** 11 **E** 12 **L**   [10]

7 (One point for each underlined answer.)
You asked about next week. I'm afraid I'm very busy. On Monday morning I'm flying to Edinburgh, because I'm seeing Patricia about some videos. Martina and Erica are going too. I'm coming back on Wednesday evening, and I can see you then – but I think you're going to Berlin on Wednesday. I'm flying to Ottawa next Friday. How long are you staying in Berlin?
Are you coming back next week? Maybe we can meet on Thursday evening.   [7]

8 (One point for each underlined answer.)
What are in the morning this morning
How long is she staying? She's staying for a week. She's leaving on Monday.
What a lovely dress! What lovely dresses!
Can I try it on? try them on?
Can you give me a Size 12? I'll pay by cheque.   [12]

Unit 12

1 1 park 2 library 3 zoo 4 canteen 5 airport 6 conference room   [6]

2 1 It says you mustn't pick the flowers. 2 It says you mustn't talk when other people are working. 3 It says you mustn't feed the animals. 4 It says you must put your cups and saucers here. 5 It says you must arrive at least an hour before the plane leaves. 6 It says you must show identity cards at reception.   [6]

3 1 to 2 a 3 some 4 to 5 some 6 to 7 to 8 a 9 some   [9]

4 hated dropped typed arrived played watched looked started walked wanted travelled finished   [12]

5 1 Do not 2 must not 3 do not 4 must not 5 are not 6 can not (or cannot) 7 does not 8 is not 9 did not 10 do not   [10]

6 1 lose/find 2 large/small 3 boring/interesting 4 arrive/leave 5 start/finish 6 before/after 7 north/south 8 a little/a lot 9 tomorrow/yesterday 10 fast/slow   [10]

7 1 No. Tell him not to bring a lot of money. 2 No. Tell them to stay at the hotel. 3 No. Tell her to stay at the hotel, too. 4 No. Tell them to phone him tomorrow evening. 5 No. Tell him not to bring the photographs. 6 Yes. Tell him to bring the books.   [6]

8 1 Did you have a good day at the shops? 2 Did you have a good meal at the restaurant? 3 Did you have a nice holiday in Spain? 4 Did you enjoy your evening at the theatre? 5 Did you like the hotel in Scotland? 6 Did you enjoy your weekend in the country? *[6]*

9 1 Tell him to sit down. 2 Tell her not to go. 3 Tell them not to stay. 4 Please talk quietly. 5 Don't park here. 6 You mustn't touch. 7 You must leave soon. 8 Sit in this chair. 9 We stayed in a hotel. 10 Did you have a good time? *[10]*

Unit 13

1 1 Are you? 2 Do you? 3 Are you? 4 Is she? 5 Does she? 6 Is she? 7 Are you? 8 Are they? 9 Do they? 10 Did they? *[10]*

2 1 Aren't you a student? 2 Isn't your name Margaret? 3 Aren't you a friend of Suzanne's? 4 Isn't Suzanne in Canada now? 5 Isn't she coming back soon? 6 Didn't you meet her at Patsy's party? 7 Aren't you staying at Suzanne's house? 8 Aren't you studying films? 9 Don't you want to be a film director? 10 Aren't you leaving Britain soon? *[10]*

3 1 Can you ask the milkman to leave one pint of milk on Saturday? 2 Can you ask Mum and Dad not to come on Thursday? 3 Can you ask Mr Harris to pick up my letters? 4 Can you ask Mrs Greenley to look after the cat? 5 Can you ask Mrs Waters to stop the newspapers for a week? 6 Can you ask Peter and Paula not to come on Wednesday? 7 Can you ask the children not to play in the sitting room? 8 Can you ask Patrick to phone me in Manchester? 9 Can you ask Patrick not to phone me before eight o'clock? 10 Can you ask Mr Harris to send my letters to Manchester? *[10]*

4 1 a) 2 b) 3 a) 4 a) 5 b) 6 c) *[6]*

5 walked said played started left paid got stole came sat lost told saw finished liked drove *[16]*

6 1 Did you finish 2 She didn't get 3 We played 4 Your friend didn't leave 5 When did the film start? 6 It started 7 When did they go? 8 They went 9 I didn't pay 10 How much did you pay? 11 We paid 12 They liked 13 Did you like 14 They came 15 When did they come? *[15]*

7

	Regular	Irregular
Positive	waited	paid
Negative	wait	pay
Questions	wait	pay
Negative questions	wait	pay *[8]*

Unit 14

1 1 I've bought the sugar, but I haven't bought the milk yet. 2 They've had breakfast, but they haven't had a shower yet. 3 He's been to the bank, but he hasn't been to the tourist office yet. 4 He's seen the park, but he hasn't seen the river yet. 5 I've phoned the airport, but I haven't phoned the station yet. 6 I've talked to Ms Harvey, but I haven't talked to Ms Jenkinson yet. *[6]*

2 1 (I think) the Mexicans are going to be second. 2 That's right. They aren't going to come. 3 Yes, we're going to make another film. 4 No, I'm going to start in September. 5 No. Diana and I are going to make it. 6 That's right. He's going to work with her. 7 I'm going to have a holiday. *[7]*

3 1 How long have you lived in London? 2 How long have you worked for this company? 3 How long has your mother worked here? 4 How long have your parents lived in London? 5 How long has your father been a teacher? 6 How long has he been at Tottenham School? *[6]*

4 1 Are you going to see Judith there? 2 Is Judith going to stay in the Tower Hotel? 3 Are Judith's assistants going to be there? 4 Are they going to talk to Mr Devine? 5 Is Mr Devine going to fly to Paris next month? 6 Are you going to see him in London? 7 Are we going to have a meeting with him in New York? 8 Am I going to see you before the meeting? 9 Are Mary and Peter going to come to the meeting in New York? 10 Are they going to stay with you? *[10]*

5 1 his 2 his 3 hers 4 mine 5 theirs 6 their 7 theirs 8 yours *[8]*

6 Mary's **S** the children's **P** the dogs' **P** the girl's **S** the doctor's **S** the teachers' **P** the Smiths' **P** the teacher's **S** the women's **P** the men's **P** *[10]*

7 **(One point for each correct answer.)**
She's eaten. We've eaten. They've eaten.
You haven't eaten. He hasn't eaten. She hasn't eaten. We haven't eaten. They haven't eaten.
Have you met him? Has he met him? Has she met him? Have we met him? Have they met him?
You're going to leave soon. He's going to leave soon. She's going to leave soon. We're going to leave soon. They're going to leave soon.
You aren't going to see her. He isn't going to see her. She isn't going to see her. We aren't going to see her. They aren't going to see her.
Are you going to visit them? Is he going to visit them? Is she going to visit them? Are we going to visit them? Are they going to visit them? *[28]*

Unit 15

1 1 She left here at three. 2 He stayed for hours. 3 Mrs Harris liked the film. 4 We went to the shops in the evening. 5 We took sandwiches to school. 6 The children played football on Saturday. 7 They drank a lot of coffee. 8 I played chess with Margaret. 9 You didn't come to see me very often. 10 They didn't like sightseeing very much. *[10]*

2 1 a) 2 a) 3 a) 4 b) 5 a) 6 a) 7 b) 8 a) 9 a) 10 b) *[10]*

3 **(One point for each full stop, capital letter, or apostrophe.)**
Most of the boys' mothers are coming and all of the girls' fathers. The parents are very worried. Everybody likes the children's teacher and they all want her to stay. They are coming to the parents' meeting to hear Miss Greenley's decision. She's going to give the school's answer tonight. *[19]*

4 1 in 2 at 3 – 4 on (*or* –) 5 into 6 at 7 – 8 into 9 on 10 in *[10]*

5 1 is 2 has 3 is 4 has 5 has 6 is 7 is 8 is 9 has 10 is *[10]*

6 1 hers 2 his 3 mine 4 yours 5 theirs 6 ours *[6]*

7 1 Are you? 2 Do you? 3 Can you? 4 Is it? 5 Did you? 6 Have you? 7 Are you? 8 Are you? 9 Does it? 10 Does it? *[10]*

Prepositions

8 Write *to, by, in,* or *at* in the spaces.

My name's Kevin Tandey and I live ....in.......... Manchester. I'm a student .... Manchester College of Art. I'm staying .... a hostel some miles from the centre of town. I usually go .... college .... bus, but sometimes I go .... car. It takes about half an hour.

.... the weekend I usually stay .... my room and work. I like talking .... the other students, and we sometimes go .... a disco or a pub, but I usually stay .... home and study. I like my work, it's interesting.

Grammar summary

9 Write these words in the correct places in the tables below.

    is does takes would 'd go goes every take a 's do does

How far ....is........ it?	How long ....does........ the journey ....?
It .... about a mile.	It .... about ten minutes.

How	.... you	
	.... he/she	get to work?
I always/usually/often/sometimes/ .... by car.		
He/She always/usually/often/sometimes/ .... by bus.		

	.... day.
How often do you go by bus?	Once Twice .... week.

.... you like a sandwich or some salad?
Yes, please. I .... like a sandwich.

Unit 9

The past simple

Questions			*Short answers*					
Did	I you he she we they	like the film?	Yes,	I you he she we they	did.	No,	I you he she we they	didn't.

Ask questions

1 **Write the questions.**

(you/enjoy/your sightseeing?)

<u>Did you enjoy your sightseeing?</u>

1 (you/like/the parks?)

....

2 (you/like/the Tower of London?)

....

3 (your parents/enjoy the sightseeing?)

....

4 (they/like/the Tower?)

....

5 (your sister/like/the cafes?)

....

6 (Peter/enjoy/the/meal?)

....

Give answers

2 **Write the short answers in the bubbles.**

Did you enjoy the party? — No, *I didn't.*

Did Martin like London? — Yes, *he did.*

1 Did you enjoy the programme? — No, ...

2 Did Patrick like the film? — Yes, ...

3 Did your friends enjoy their holiday? — No, ...

4 Did they like the hotel? — Yes, ...

5 Did Mrs Harrison enjoy the conference? — Yes, ...

6 Did her husband enjoy it? — No, ...

7 Did you like Mr Harrison? — No, ...

8 Did Sue like him? — Yes, ...

3 Write the answers in full
(✓ = positive, ✗ = negative).

Did you like the people at the party?
✓ Sue and George ✗ their friends

Not really. _I liked Sue and George,_

but I didn't like their friends.

1 Didn't you like Pat and Mark?
✓ Pat and Mark ✗ the others

Yes, _I liked_ ....

....

2 Was the music good?
✓ reggae ✗ other music

Well, _I liked_ ....

....

3 Was it a nice house?
✓ garden ✗ house

....

....

4 How about Sue's children?
✓ her daughter ✗ her sons

....

....

5 How about the meal in the restaurant?
✓ the restaurant ✗ the food

....

....

Which is which?

Would like + noun or verb	
Would you like	*Noun* a chocolate? some water? *Verb* to go home? to come with me?

4 Write *V* by the verbs, and *N* by the nouns.

go .....V..... sit .... see ....

cake ....N.... beef .... pen ....

come .... listen .... beer ....

take .... lunch .... ask ....

cup .... fruit ....

5 Write *a*, *some* or *to* in the gaps.

Would you like ....to.... go to a restaurant?

Would you like ..some.. tea?

1 Would you like .... come with us?

2 Would you like .... beef?

3 Would you like .... see the cathedral?

4 Would you like .... take a taxi?

5 Would you like .... listen to some records?

6 Would you like .... pen?

7 Would you like .... cup?

8 Would you like .... lunch?

9 Would you like .... beer?

10 Would you like .... sit here?

Unit 9

Use numbers

6 Write the numbers in the boxes.

see you on the fourteenth → `14th`

meet Maggie on the third → `3rd`

Conference-thirtieth → 1. ☐

Pat's birthday—on the seventeenth! → 2. ☐

Don't forget the meeting on the second of June. → 3. ☐

It's on the first of May! → 4. ☐

She's arriving on the fourth of March. → 5. ☐

I think it's the twentieth. → 6. ☐

My birthday is on the fifteenth → 7. ☐

NOT THE THIRTY-FIRST! → 8. ☐

Prepositions

On, In + days and months	
On	
Days	**Dates**
on Tuesday	on 18th May
on Friday	on 1st June
In	
Months	**Seasons**
in May	in (the) spring
in April	in (the) summer

7 Write *in* or *on* in the spaces.

Her birthday's .... on .... Tuesday.

It was .... in .... the spring.

1 My birthday's .... 22nd March.

2 I think the meeting's .... May.

3 The party was .... Tuesday.

4 The garden's lovely .... the summer.

5 I like the house .... the autumn.

6 The next meeting is .... Thursday 17th October.

7 My birthday's .... September.

34

Grammar summary

8 Write the missing words.

The past simple

Positive		
I	....enjoyed....	(enjoy) the sightseeing.
You	....liked....	(like) the food.
He	....	(enjoy) the dancing.
She	....	(like) the music.
We	....	(enjoy) our holiday.
They	....	(like) us.

Negative		
I	..didn't like..	(like) Margaret.
You	didn't enjoy	(enjoy) the party.
Paul	....	(enjoy) the concert.
Sue	....	(like) Paul.
We	....	(like) the music.
They	....	(like) my records.

Questions			
....Did....	I	....enjoy....	(enjoy) the film?
....Did....	you	....like....	(like) the record?
....	he	....	(enjoy) the party?
....	she	....	(like) the concert?
....	we	....	(enjoy) our holiday?
....	they	....	(like) your friends?

Short answers				
Positive			*Negative*	
Yes, I	....did.....		No, I	....didn't....
you	....did.....		you	....didn't....
he	....did.....		he	....
she	....		she	....
we	....		we	....
they	....		they	....

1 Write this passage with capital letters, full stops, and apostrophes.

peter parry isnt working hes unemployed he lives in a friends house in london he doesnt like london because its too big he wants to go back to liverpool but he cant because there are no jobs there liverpool is still his favourite town

Peter Parry isn't working.

....

....

....

....

....

....

....

....

2 Write *is*, *are*, *do* or *does* in the spaces.

............Do............ you usually walk to work?

1 .... you always watch television in the evening?

2 .... you working?

3 .... he looking after his sister?

4 How often .... she go abroad?

5 What .... you eating?

6 Which restaurant .... you like?

7 Where .... he live?

8 What .... they doing?

9 ....Is............ Paul staying here?

10 How long ....does............ it take?

3 Write *was*, *were* or *did*.

▇▇ you enjoy last night? ....Did............

1 I ▇▇n't enjoy the film. ....

2 The cinema ▇▇n't very nice. ....

3 The tickets ▇▇ expensive. ....

4 My parents ▇▇n't like the restaurant. ....

5 The vegetables ▇▇ fine. ....

6 The meat ▇▇n't very nice. ....

7 There ▇▇n't any taxis. ....

8 The bus ▇▇n't come. ....

4 Write the numbers.

two hundred pounds

1 .... 6 ....

2 .... 7 ....

3 .... 8 ....

4 .... 9 ....

5 .... 10 ....

5 Complete the box.

Subject	Object	Adjective
I	me	my
you		
he		
she		
it		
we		
they		

6 Circle the correct answer.

What sort of salad a) *are* b) *were* c) *would* you like?

1 a) *Have* b) *Has* c) *Is* you got any sisters?
2 Would you like a a) *tea* b) *piece* c) *cup* of coffee?
3 a) *Were* b) *Was* c) *Did* Diana at home last night?
4 I want to buy a) *a* b) *an* c) *some* milk.
5 What time a) *is* b) *does* c) *has* the bus leave school?
6 There aren't a) *a* b) *some* c) *any* tickets.
7 I'm a student a) *at* b) *on* c) *by* Manchester College.
8 Her birthday's a) *in* b) *at* c) *on* Thursday.
9 How much are a) *this* b) *that* c) *those* shoes?
10 I usually go home a) *with* b) *by* c) *on* bus.

7 Match the questions and answers.

A What are you doing?
B How far is it to Edinburgh?
C Why didn't you like the film?
D How often does she go abroad?
E Is there a bank near here?
F What's the weather like?
G Isn't it a lovely day?
H What shall we do today?

A

Yes, there's one over there.

Let's go to the beach.

About thirty miles.

Yes, it's very nice.

It was too long.

I'm reading.

About once a month.

It's raining.

Unit 11

Ask questions

1 Write the questions.

Why/go/Athens? _Why are you going to Athens?_ .... To see Judith.

1 When/go? .... Tomorrow.

2 Which airport/leave from? .... Heathrow.

3 How long/stay in Athens? .... For three days.

4 Where/stay? .... With some friends.

5 When/come back? .... On Thursday.

6 What time/arriving? .... 23.45.

7 How/get home? .... By taxi.

8 When/see/Mrs Harris? .... Next week.

2 Write the sentences in the correct bubbles.

38

Give answers

3 Write short answers using *Yes*.

Are you seeing Samantha next week?

Yes, I am.

1 Is the meeting in London?

....

2 Are Jayne and Maria coming too?

....

3 Is Nick flying here from Mexico?

....

4 Is Samantha coming by plane?

....

5 Are you seeing them at the Tower Hotel?

....

6 Are you all going to the computer conference?

....

7 Is Nick going to the conference too?

....

8 Are they all going home on Thursday?

....

Word formation

Plurals				
	Singular			*Plural*
Most words	cat dog friend ticket school		+ s	cats dogs friends tickets schools
Words ending in -y	baby country secretary		+ ies	babies countries secretaries
Words ending in -ay, -oy, -ey	day boy journey		+ s	days boys journeys
Words ending in -ss or -ch	church glass watch		+ es	churches glasses watches

4 Write the plurals of the words in the boxes.

airport	airports	holiday	
library	libraries	video	
church	churches	beach	
tour		cinema	
journey		glass	
coach		dance	
city		boy	
key		window	
family		cheque	

Unit 11

Use your dictionary

> **Checking plurals in the dictionary**
>
> Most nouns add *s* to make a plural.
> Some nouns add *es* or *ies*.   (See Exercise 4.)
>
> A small number of plurals are irregular
> (=don't follow these rules). They are shown
> in the dictionary like this:
>
> **child** /tʃaɪld/ *n* **children** /'tʃɪldrən/
>
> **to·ma·to** /təˈmɑːtəʊ‖-ˈmeɪ-/ *n* -**toes**

5 Some of these words have regular plurals.
Others are irregular. Use your dictionary, and
write the plurals in the boxes.

girl	*girls*
child	*children*
1 woman	
2 programme	
3 housewife	
4 potato	
5 relative	
6 day	
7 man	
8 cassette	
9 dress	
10 disco	

Language in use

6 Put the conversation in the correct order.

A   Size 14, I think.
B   Yes. Can I have a look at those shirts?
C   Size 14. That's a Medium. Here you are.
D   Can I help you?
E   It's lovely. I'll take it. Can I pay by cheque?
F   It's nice, but a bit big. Can you give me a 12, please?
G   The shirts? Of course you can.
H   What lovely shirts!
I   Certainly. What size are you?
J   They're nice. Can I try that green one on?
K   12 . . . try a Small.
L   Yes, of course. Cheques are fine.

1	2	3	4	5	6	7	8	9	10	11	12
H	D										

7 Complete the letter. Write the verbs in the present continuous.

> You asked about next week. I'm afraid
> I'm very busy. On Monday morning
> I ....'m flying.(fly) to Edinburgh,
> because I ....(see) Patricia
> about some videos. Martin and Erica
> ....(go) too. I ....
> (come) back on Wednesday evening, and I
> can see you then – but I think you ......
> ....(go) to Berlin on Wednesday.
> I ....(fly) to Ottawa next
> Friday. How long ....
> (you stay) in Berlin? ....
> (you come) back next week? Maybe we can
> meet on Thursday evening.

Grammar summary

8 Write these words in the correct boxes.

I'll   for   on   in   this   next   What   them
Can I   Can you   What a   How long   What are

	you they	doing	........**next**........ summer?
			.... the morning?
....			on Saturday?
			.... morning?

.... is she staying?	She's staying .... a week.
	She's leaving .... Monday.

.... lovely dress!	....	try it on?
.... lovely dresses!		try .... on?

.... give me a size 12?	.... pay by cheque.

Unit 12

Language in use

1 Where do you see these signs? Match the signs with the places

cafe   airport   canteen   park   library   conference room   zoo

| PLEASE DO NOT SMOKE IN THESE SEATS | DO NOT PICK THE FLOWERS | PLEASE DO NOT TALK WHEN OTHER PEOPLE ARE WORKING | PLEASE DO NOT FEED THE ANIMALS |

.... cafe .... 1 .... 2 .... 3 ....

| PLEASE PUT YOUR CUPS AND SAUCERS HERE | PLEASE ARRIVE AT LEAST ONE HOUR BEFORE YOUR PLANE LEAVES | Please show identity cards at reception |

4 .... 5 .... 6 ....

2 Sylvie is explaining the signs to her brother, because he can't read. Use *must* or *mustn't* to explain the signs above.

What does this sign say?

It says you mustn't smoke in these seats. ....

1 What does this sign say?

   ....

2 How about this one? What does this say?

   ....

3 Can you see this sign? What does it say?

   ....

4 This is a funny sign.

   ....

5 And this one?

   ....

6 And what about this one?

   ....

42

3 Write *a*, *some* or *to* in the spaces.

Would you like ......to...... go in my car?

1 Would you like .... come with me?

2 Would you like .... new ticket?

3 Would you like .... coffee?

4 Would you like .... borrow my coat?

5 Would you like .... money?

6 Would you like .... wait here?

7 Would you like .... try on this sweater?

8 Would you like .... lift to the station?

9 Would you like .... fresh air?

Use your dictionary

The past simple: regular verbs

Positive
Most verbs add *ed* to make the past simple positive:

| stay | + **ed** | = stayed |
| wait | + **ed** | = waited |

Verbs ending in *e* add only *d*:

| like | + **d** | = liked |
| hate | + **d** | = hated |

Some (but not all) verbs ending in **one** vowel + **one** consonant double the final consonant. Check in your dictionary.

| drop | dropped |
| stop | stopped |

drop² *v* -pp- 1 [I;T] to fall or let fall:

Long and short

Don't/Mustn't

n't is short for *not:*
don't = do not, mustn't = must not
isn't = is not, can't = can not

The short form is used in informal or conversational English.
The long form is used in formal, written English (often on notices or signs).

5 Write the long form of the words in the boxes.

Don't smoke in this room.

1 Don't tell Peter.

2 You mustn't sit in here.

3 Please don't drop litter.

4 You mustn't be late.

5 They aren't very well.

6 She can't type.

7 He doesn't like me.

8 Diana isn't going.

9 We didn't like the film.

10 I don't understand.

Do not

4 Write the past simple positive of these verbs.

wait	waited	play	
like	liked	watch	
stop	stopped	look	
		start	
hate		walk	
drop		want	
type		travel	
arrive		finish	

Unit 12

Language in use

6 Match the words in Box A with their opposite meanings in Box B.

A	B
question	finish
lose	answer
large	after
boring	small
arrive	interesting
start	leave
before	find
north	south
a little	yesterday
tomorrow	a lot
fast	slow

    question   /   answer

1 .... / ....

2 .... / ....

3 .... / ....

4 .... / ....

5 .... / ....

6 .... / ....

7 .... / ....

8 .... / ....

9 .... / ....

10 .... / ....

7 Complete the telephone conversation.

Jack's arriving at ten tomorrow. Can you meet him?

(Yes/wait by the ticket office)
Yes, tell him to wait by the ticket office.

1 Does he need a lot of money?

(No/not bring a lot of money)
....
....

2 Colin and John want to see him. Can they come?

(No/stay at the hotel)
....
....

3 How about Louise?

(No/stay at the hotel, too.)
....
....

4 Can they see him tonight?

(No/phone him tomorrow morning)
....
....

5 Jack wants to bring the photographs.

(No/not bring the photographs)
....
....

6 How about the books?

(Yes/bring the books)
....
....

44

Ask questions

8 Write the sentences in the correct order.

a good/have/did/in/you/time/Cambridge/?

Did you have a good time in Cambridge?

1 day/you/the shops/a good/have/at/did/?

....

2 have/meal/the restaurant/a good/you/did/at/?

....

3 you/a/Spain/did/have/nice/holiday/in/?

....

4 at/your/you/theatre/the/evening/enjoy/did/?

....

5 in/like/did/hotel/you/the/Scotland/?

....

6 you/your weekend/the/in/enjoy/did/country/?

....

Grammar summary

9 Write the sentences in the correct order.

here/sit/must/you	*You must sit here.*
1 down/to/him/sit/tell	....
2 her/to/not/go/tell	....
3 to/stay/tell/them/not	....
4 quietly/please/talk	....
5 here/park/don't	....
6 touch/mustn't/you	....
7 leave/soon/must/you	....
8 chair/this/in/sit	....
9 a/hotel/stayed/in/we	....
10 have/you/a/good/time/did?	....

Unit 13

Ask questions

1 **Write short questions to show surprise.**

I'm French. — Are you ?

1 I'm 42. — ....

2 I live in Italy. — ....

3 I'm a doctor. — ....

4 My sister's a doctor, too. — ....

5 She lives in New York. — ....

6 She's going to Rome tomorrow. — ....

7 I'm meeting her there. — ....

8 Our parents are coming, too. — ....

9 They live in Morocco. — ....

10 They flew here yesterday. — ....

2 **Check information by asking negative questions.**

I think . . .

you're German.
Aren't you German? ....

1 you're a student.

....

2 your name's Margaret.

....

3 you're a friend of Suzanne's.

....

4 Suzanne's in Canada now.

....

5 she's coming back soon.

....

6 you met her at Patsy's party.

....

7 you're staying at Suzanne's house.

....

8 you're studying films.

....

9 you want to be a film director.

....

10 you're leaving Britain soon.

....

46

Language in use

3 Your brother is looking after your house. Give him instructions.

milkman/not/leave any milk this week

Can you ask the milkman not to
leave any milk this week?

police/check the house every day

Can you ask the police to check
the house every day?

1 milkman/leave one pint of milk on Saturday

....
....

2 Mum and Dad/not/come on Thursday

....
....

3 Mr Harris/pick up my letters

....
....

4 Mrs Greenley/look after the cat

....
....

5 Mrs Waters/stop the newspapers for a week

....
....

6 Peter and Paula/not/come on Wednesday

....
....

7 The children/not play in the sitting room

....
....

8 Patrick/phone me in Manchester

....
....

9 Patrick/not/phone me before eight o'clock

....
....

10 Mr Harris/send my letters to Manchester

....
....

4 Circle the correct answer.

I didn't see *a) no one* (b)) *any one* *c) nothing*.

1 *a) Someone* *b) Any one* *c) Nothing* broke into my flat.

2 They took *a) everywhere* *b) everything* *c) no one*.

3 I looked *a) everywhere* *b) nothing* *c) everybody* for my dog.

4 I put *a) everything* *b) everyone* *c) no one* in the bag.

5 Would you like *a) nothing* *b) something* *c) someone* to eat?

6 Didn't you see *a) no one* *b) nothing* *c) anything*?

Unit 13

Use your dictionary

The past simple

Negative
All verbs are regular in the past simple negative:
  I didn't enjoy it. | She didn't go.
  She didn't like me. | He didn't find it.

Questions
All verbs are regular in the past simple question:
  Did you enjoy it. | Did she go?
  Did she like me? | Did he find it?

Positive
Regular verbs add *ed* or *d*. (See Unit 12 Exercise 4.) | About 100 verbs are irregular. (Check in your dictionary.)
  I enjoyed the film. | She went.
  She liked me. | **go¹** /gəʊ/ *v* **went** /went/,

5   Write the past simple positive of these verbs:

finish	finished	steal	
go	went	come	
walk		sit	
say		lose	
play		tell	
start		see	
leave		finish	
pay		like	
get		drive	

6   Write the correct form of the past simple.

Did you ...... **see** ...... (see) anybody?

I didn't ...... **see** ...... (see) him.

I ...... **saw** ...... (see) him yesterday.

1   Did you .... (finish) the book?

2   She didn't .... (get) the money.

3   We .... (play) chess for hours.

4   Your friend didn't .... (leave) any
                   money.

5   When did the film .... (start)?

6   It .... (start) at five o'clock.

7   When did they .... (go)?

8   They .... (go) at half-past ten.

9   I didn't .... (pay) him.

10   How much did you .... (pay)?

11   We .... (pay) a lot of money.

12   They .... (like) the food.

13   Did you .... (like) the hotel?

14   They .... (come) yesterday.

15   When did they .... (come)?

Grammar summary

7 Write these words in the correct boxes.

wait   wait   wait   waited
pay   pay   pay   paid

The past simple: regular and irregular verbs

Positive

Regular
I
You
He
She .... for him.
We
They

Irregular
I
You
He
She .... the bill.
We
They

Negative

Regular
I
You
He
She didn't .... for him.
We
They

Irregular
I
You
He
She didn't .... the bill.
We
They

Positive questions

Regular

Did
I
you
he
she .... for him?
we
they

Irregular

Did
I
you
he
she .... the bill?
we
they

Negative questions

Regular

Didn't
I
you
he
she .... for him?
we
they

Irregular

Didn't
I
you
he
she .... the bill?
we
they

Unit 14

Give answers

1 Write the answers to the questions (✓ = positive, ✗ = negative).

Have you bought the tea yet?
(tea ✓   coffee ✗)

I've bought the tea, but I haven't bought the coffee yet.

1   Have you bought the sugar yet?
    (sugar ✓   milk ✗)

    ....

    ....

2   Have the children had breakfast yet?
    (breakfast ✓   a shower ✗)

    ....

    ....

3   Has Richard been to the bank yet?
    (bank ✓   tourist office ✗)

    ....

    ....

4   Has he seen the park yet?
    (park ✓   river ✗)

    ....

    ....

5   Have you phoned the airport yet?
    (airport ✓   station ✗)

    ....

    ....

6   Have you talked to Ms Harvey yet?
    (Ms Harvey ✓   Ms Jenkinson ✗)

    ....

    ....

2 Complete the conversation, using *going to*.

So you think you and Diana are going to win?

(we/win) Yes. I think we're going to win.

How about the Americans?

(they/not/win) No. They aren't going to win.

1   Who's going to be second?

    (the Mexicans/be second) ....

    ....

2   And the Canadians aren't going to come?

    (they/not/come) That's right. ....

    ....

3   Are you going to make another film?

    (we/make/film) Yes. ....

    ....

4   Oh. When are you going to start? Next year?

    (I/start in September) No. ....

    ....

5   Who's going to make it? All three of you?

    (Diana and I/make it). No. ....

    ....

6   Is Peter going to work with Lesley again?

    (he/work with her) That's right. He ....

    ....

7   What are you going to do after the conference?

    (I/have a holiday) ....

    ....

Ask questions

3 Write the questions, using *How long*.

How long have
you lived here?

I've lived here
for twenty years.

1 ....

I've lived in London
for three years.

2 ....

I've worked for this
company for seven
months.

3 ....

My mother's worked
here for over fifteen
years.

4 ....

My parents have
lived in London
for fifty years.

5 ....

My father's been
a teacher for
twenty years.

6 ....

He's been at
Tottenham School
for eighteen months.

4 Write questions, using *going to*.

you/fly/to London next week?
Are you going to fly to London
next week?

1 you/see/Judith there?

....

2 Judith/stay/in the Tower Hotel?

....

3 Judith's assistants/be there?

....

4 they/talk to/Mr Devine?

....

5 Mr Devine/fly to Paris/next month?

....

6 you/see him/in London?

....

7 we/have a meeting with him in New York?

....

8 I/see you before the meeting?

....

9 Mary and Peter/come to the meeting.

....

10 they/stay with you?

....

Word formation

> **Possessive adjectives and possessive pronouns**
>
> | | | | | | | | |
> |---|---|---|---|---|---|---|---|
> | *Adjectives* | my | your | his | her | its | our | their |
> | *Pronouns* | mine | yours | his | hers | — | ours | theirs |
>
> Possessive adjectives go before a noun: It's my school.
> Possessive pronouns stand alone: It's mine.

5 Write the correct pronoun or adjective in the space.

Give it to me. It's ....*my*........ money.

Give it to me. It's ......*mine*...... .

1 Give it to your father. It's .... book.

2 Give it to your father. It's ....

3 Take this to Mrs Harris, please. It's ....

4 Q: Is this your car?

   A: Yes, it's ....

5 Q: Are these Barry and Cathy's coats?

   A: Yes, I think they are ....

6 Q: Can you see the Flemings' house?

   A: Yes, ... house is over there.

7 Q: Is this the Flemings' dog?

   A: Yes, I think it's ....

8 I think this is your room. Is it ....?

Punctuation

> **The apostrophe**
>
> *Singular*
> The apostrophe goes before the *s:*
> the girl → the girl's school
> Mary → Mary's purse
>
> *Plural*
> The apostrophe goes after the *s:*
> the boys → the boys' school
> the Smiths → the Smiths' car
>
> *Irregular plurals*
> the children → the children's school
> the men → the men's work
> the women → the women's jobs

6 Write *S* for singular nouns, and *P* for plural.

the animals' home	P	the doctor's car	
the animal's home	S	the teachers' room	
Mary's brother		the Smiths' house	
the children's game		the teacher's car	
the dogs' food		the women's club	
the girl's mother		the men's game	

Grammar summary

7 Write the missing words.

The present perfect

Positive

I	've	
You	've	
He	's	
She	....	eaten.
We	....	
They	....	

Negative

I	haven't	
You	....	
He	....	
She	....	eaten (yet).
We	....	
They	....	

Questions

Have	I	
....	you	
....	he	
....	she	met him?
....	we	
....	they	

Going to

Positive

I	'm going to	
You	....	
He	....	
She	....	leave soon.
We	....	
They	....	

Negative

I	'm not going to	
You	....	
He	....	
She	....	see her.
We	....	
They	....	

Questions

Am	I	
....	you	
....	he	
....	she	going to visit them?
....	we	
....	they	

Unit 15 Consolidation

1 Write these sentences in the past simple.

He leaves his house at nine o'clock.

He left his house at nine o'clock.

1 She leaves here at three.

....

2 He stays for hours.

....

3 Mrs Harris likes the film.

....

4 We go to the shops in the evening.

....

....

5 We take sandwiches to school.

....

6 The children play football on Saturday.

....

....

7 They drink a lot of coffee.

....

8 I play chess with Margaret.

....

9 You don't come to see me very often.

....

....

10 They don't like sightseeing very much.

....

....

2 Circle the correct answer.

I *a) haven't done* b) didn't do my homework yet.

1 a) Have you b) Did you tidied your room yet?

2 They a) cleared up b) 've clreared up last night.

3 I a) haven't finished b) didn't finished yet.

4 We a) 've invited b) invited last week.

5 a) Have they b) Did they got married yet?

6 How long a) have you been b) did you here?

7 a) Did you heard b) Have you heard from your office yet?

8 When a) was b) has been the conference?

9 She a) was b) has been here yesterday.

10 I a) have seen b) saw them last night.

3 Write this passage with full stops, capital letters, and apostrophes.

were inviting a lot of people to the school most of the boys mothers are coming and all of the girls fathers the parents are very worried everybody likes the childrens teacher and they all want her to stay they are coming to the parents meeting to hear miss greenleys decision shes going to give the schools answer tonight.

We're inviting a lot of people to the school.

....

....

....

....

....

....

....

....

4 Write *in, on, at, into* or – in the spaces.

She ran ......*into*...... the cathedral.

We went ......–...... home.

1 I live .... Mexico City.

2 I'm going to meet her .... the airport.

3 Have you phoned .... Jean yet?

4 I haven't tried them .... yet.

5 The girls walked .... the room.

6 Can I have a look .... those shirts?

7 I'm going .... home.

8 You mustn't take food .... the church.

9 I'm going to see them .... Sunday.

10 They visited us .... February.

5 Write *is* or *has* in the box.

She's been here for hours. | has |

1 He's arriving tomorrow. | |

2 He's had lunch. | |

3 She's a teacher. | |

4 Paul's been to Paris. | |

5 He's got a large family. | |

6 She's going to phone next week. | |

7 Mark's going to send me the money soon. | |

8 It's raining. | |

9 My mother's worked here for seven years. | |

10 It's about thirty miles. | |

6 Complete the sentences.

Is this your sports bag? I think it's ...*yours.*...

1 Is this Mary's suitcase? I think it's ....

2 Is this Peter's bag? Yes, it's ....

3 I think this is my newspaper. Is it ....?

4 This is your book, I think. It is ...., isn't it?

5 I think this is their house. Is it ....?

6 Are these our seats? I think they're ....

7 Write short questions.

I'm forty-seven. → *Are you* ....?

1 I'm French. → ....?

2 I like London. → ....?

3 I can speak English. → ....?

4 It's easy. → ....?

5 I lived here last year. → ....?

6 I've been to Scotland, too. → ....?

7 I'm going again soon. → ....?

8 I'm flying there tomorrow. → ....?

9 It takes an hour. → ....?

10 The book finishes here. → ....?

Grammar index

This index includes grammatical terms (in normal type) and English words and phrases (*in italic type*).

Grammar score chart

To check your grammar scores, mark your totals for each unit on the chart.

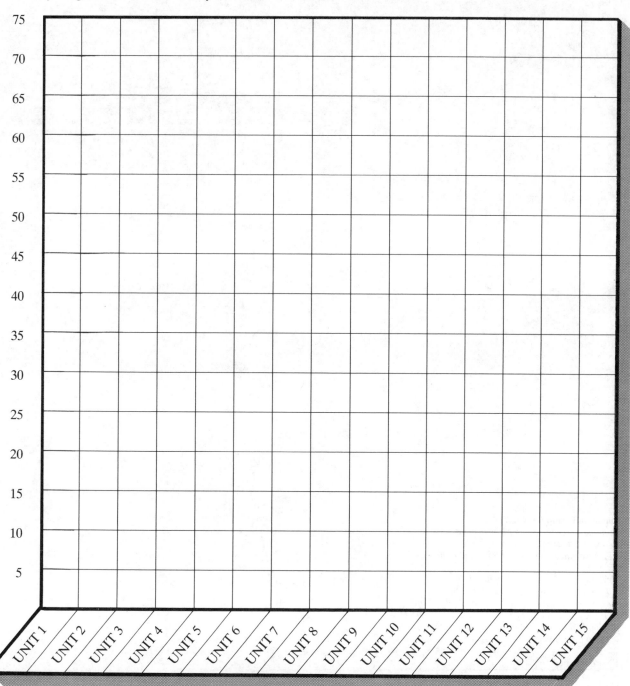

Longman Group UK Limited,
Longman House, Burnt Mill, Harlow,
Essex CM20 2JE, England
and Associated Companies throughout the world.

First published 1988

Set in 10/11 Linotron Times
Printed in Italy
by Milanostampa, Farigliano (CN)

ISBN 0-582-01407-7